PETER PAN

Retold by: Arpita Barua

ILLUSTRATIONS ~ MANOJ KUREEL

Once upon a time, there lived three children called Wendy, John and Michael. They had a friend called Peter Pan.

Peter Pan was a tiny, little boy, who wore strange dresses. He could fly and was fun to be with.

Everynight, he came to visit his young friends and told them exciting stories about his adventures.

One night, the three kids asked Peter Pan to take them with him. So, Peter Pan took them to a magical place called 'Neverland'. There, they could remain as children forever.

One day in Neverland, when Peter Pan was playing with the mermaids, he asked them to come up to the surface. But the mermaids said they could not as they were afraid of the cruel Captain Hook. Peter Pan asked the mermaids, "Who is Captain Hook?"

They told him that Captain Hook was a wicked pirate. Once, a crocodile had eaten his left hand and his favourite watch.

This instance turned Captain Hook against all the sea creatures and he had decided to kill all of them.

Peter Pan decided to fight with Captain Hook and rescue the sea creatures.

Next day, when Captain Hook was sailing, Peter Pan jumped on the ship and attacked him. They both fought fiercely.

Finally, Peter Pan defeated
Captain Hook and threw him
into the sea, near a crocodile.
It was the same crocodile
that had eaten Captain
Hook's hand.

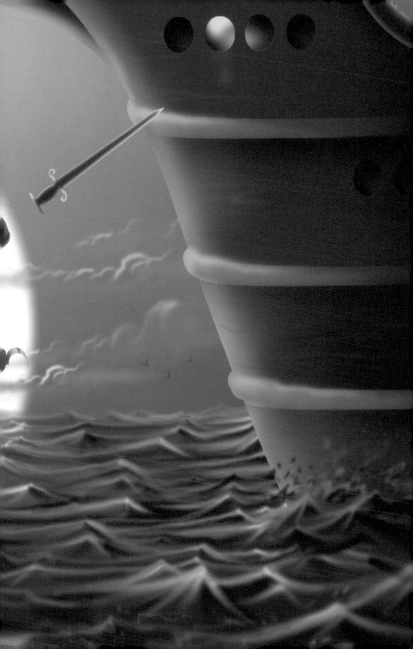

Peter Pan and his three friends celebrated the victory and played the entire day. They jumped, sang and danced in the park.

But soon Wendy became homesick. She did not want to remain a child forever and wanted to return home. She asked Peter Pan if he wanted to go with them but he refused. So, the three children said goodbye to Peter Pan and left for their home.

Wendy, Michael
and John were delighted to meet their
parents. They never left home again and
lived happily ever after.